Life *after* Boris

A FABLE ABOUT SUCCESSION PLANNING FOR PROFESSIONAL FIRMS

An enchanting, quick-to-read fable
that every current or future partner
in a mid-sized professional services firm
concerned about succession management
should read – for their own good

J A M E S   M E N D E L S S O H N
Firm Management Associates Ltd

Life after Boris: A fable about succession planning for professional firms © James Mendelssohn
ISBN 978-1-909116-04-7

Published in 2013 by SRA Books

The right of James Mendelssohn to be identified as the author of this work has been asserted by him in accordance with the Copyright, Designs and Patents Act 1988.

A CIP record of this book is available from the British Library.

Printed in the UK by TJ International, Padstow

– Contents –

– About *the* author –

Following a law degree from Cambridge and a short period in industry, James Mendelssohn spent 10 years developing the marketing functions within two major accountancy practices, both in the UK and overseas.

He then established a print and marketing consultancy, focused on the professional services sector, before taking time out to study for an MBA, with his thesis looking at management structures within international networks of professional services firms.

In 1999, James became the Chief Executive of MSI Global Alliance (MSI), a worldwide association of mid-tier law and accounting firms, with over 250 member firms in more than 100 countries. MSI won the prestigious 'International Association of the Year' award in early 2013 at the annual *International Accounting Bulletin* awards ceremony.

On stepping down from his full-time role with MSI at the end of 2012, and recognising the need that exists within many professional services firms that are struggling to come to terms with management issues, James established Firm Management Associates, a specialist consultancy focusing on providing management advice to mid-sized firms, charities and others operating in the not-for-profit sector.

Firm Management could be described as a consultancy – but James does not see himself as a consultant. He is simply someone who has worked with and observed over 250 mid-sized law and accounting firms in 100 countries and is interested in working with such firms, and other similar organisations, to explore how they could and should be managed.

If you would like further information, please do not hesitate to contact James at Firm Management Associates.

E: jmendelssohn@firmmanagement.co.uk
T: +44 (0) 7941 507753
www.firmmanagement.co.uk

– Foreword –

In the fiercely competitive business climate of today, many issues face leaders of professional firms. One issue in particular, succession planning, rarely gets the attention it deserves. Why? It is typically considered 'non-urgent' and is often side-lined or overlooked completely. Smarter firms will have a succession policy and even an HR protocol. These provide a formal framework to facilitate what can be an uncomfortable and thorny subject. This is more acutely felt in small to medium sized firms where talk of 'letting go' of the reins is often taboo and becomes the 'elephant in the room'. The fable of *Life after Boris* therefore provides a much-needed catalyst in bringing this issue to the fore.

For many firms, succession planning is neglected and is only given serious thought when an imminent senior departure looms. This is usually too late to avoid a crisis in the practice and can have some catastrophic outcomes. These may include poor client retention, a lack of management focus and damaged staff motivation.

An effective succession plan is one that addresses the gaps created by the exit of aging partners and will prepare the firm in a number of ways. It will transition existing clients over to the next generation, and it will identify and prepare the next generation with the right skills and behaviours to manage and lead the firm toward a profitable future.

All firms should seriously consider their approach to succession planning over a long-term horizon with at least a 5-year transition. It will take careful consideration and a great deal of sensitivity. It is likely to require substantive and advanced training, mentoring, and a commitment to identify and develop the future leaders.

Putting a clear succession plan together will not be easy. But for those that do recognise the dangers of neglecting this critical issue and commit to invest the time and resources to implement an effective plan, then the rewards will be significant, and will give a competitive edge over others that don't.

David Turner, Managing Director, DRT Consulting Ltd

– Introduction –

In my experience over the last 12 years of working with professional services firms around the world, one of the most frequently recurring catalysts for discussion has been succession management. Firms that got it right developed and prospered. Those that didn't struggled and often ended up having to merge and ultimately disappear into oblivion.

Succession planning is not inherently difficult or intellectually complex. It does, however, strike many raw nerves, both with those who are currently at the top of their firms and are contemplating retirement (or not), and also with those in the early stages of their careers who are anxious to know what the future holds for them in their current firm.

The frustration, of course, is that many stakeholders in the succession planning process (of which there are far more than one might originally envisage) rush into decisions because of the apparent lack of a succession plan, thereby simply exacerbating the problem for all the other stakeholders. It is therefore critical that all firms, and the stakeholders within those firms, address the succession planning question before it becomes an issue. Closing the stable door after the horse has bolted is simply not an option.

Initiating the succession planning process need not necessarily come from the current leaders. Indeed, their failure to do so is often at the root of the problem. The bright leaders of tomorrow have much at stake and although a great deal of tact and sensitivity will be needed, it is often these future leaders of a firm who are best positioned to bring about change.

Life after Boris is a quick-to-read fable that should encourage any partner – or indeed anyone aspiring to partnership – in a professional services firm, to make sure that the succession planning issue is addressed in their firm. It seeks to demonstrate that with good planning, collaboration and proactive discussion, options can be found that will be acceptable to all. Without such an approach, the consequences could be serious.

– Chapter 1 –

The ending of an era

The whispering was becoming more hushed; the rumours were spreading. Even Mrs Cabbage had been seen to wipe a tear from her eye as she left Leader Boris's room.

For Eric, a young helper in The Warren, it was clear that something was seriously wrong. Although Leader Boris had once said to him that Eric was 'a bright young rabbit with a real future', he had never elaborated and Eric was still in charge of the 'shopping' for The Warren.

Eric realised, of course, that it wasn't real shopping. He never went into a shop, and money never changed hands. The only similarity with real shopping was that he had to procure whatever it was that Mrs Cabbage asked him to procure – normally just a wonderful array of fruit and vegetables from the allotments so that she could prepare Leader Boris's favourite meals.

But Leader Boris no longer appeared to be interested in his food – and that was a really worrying sign. Instead, Mrs Cabbage had asked Eric just to bring home some radishes – and to make sure that they were the very finest radishes that the allotment could provide. Leader Boris had always liked radishes and now, it seemed, he was eating them to the exclusion of everything else.

While he was waiting outside The Warren this morning, Eric was shaken to the quick. Young Beetroot – a pretty young rabbit who was given the nickname of Beetroot (because of her propensity to blush) so long ago that nobody could remember her real name – came out and told one of the other girls that, for breakfast this morning, Leader Boris did not even want his radishes. He had a little diced lettuce, and a sip of tomato juice, and that was all he could manage before he slipped off back to sleep.

When this report filtered back to the other warrens, the rumour mill went into overdrive. That is the problem with being a rabbit, thought Eric. For reasons that he had never been able to fathom, rabbits always seemed to have very big families, and although big families can be a good thing, sometimes they can cause a problem too.

He had never forgotten the day that his half-brother, Hoppity, married his cousin. Somebody – and Eric never did discover who – made a rather unkind comment as to why Hoppity was only his half-brother and not his whole brother, and a fight developed 'to protect the honour of the family' – and then the fight turned into complete mayhem, because nobody quite knew how the family was formed and who was related to who. That is rabbits for you, thought Eric.

Leader Boris had been the head of The Warren for as long as Eric could remember – in fact, it was probably for his entire life. He couldn't imagine what would happen if Leader Boris were to die. Eric did hear one of his aunties talk about Leader Boris 'passing away'. He didn't quite know what that meant, but it sounded much less final than actually dying, so Eric did take some comfort from this.

Anyway, with no food being required for Mrs Cabbage's kitchen, Eric was not needed any more that day, so he hopped off home to get some rest and to reflect on everything that he had heard and learned over the last few days.

And the more he thought about it, the more confused his little mind became. He was a bright rabbit – everyone told him so. He had done well at school and many of the other rabbits had come to him when they needed help with their homework. He always tried to help them, because he thought it was the right thing to do. But even he, good, solid, dependable Eric was confused and not a little frightened by what the future would hold in The Warren if Leader Boris was not around. The prospect of change was rather scary.

– Chapter 2 –

Eric decides to help

Eric must have drifted off because when he opened his eyes, he could hear his mother in the kitchen getting lunch ready. His father was there too and he could hear them talking in hushed whispers.

Eric lay there for a minute, but then got to his feet purposefully. He was an adult now; he worked for Leader Boris – and he was entitled to know what was going on. As he walked into the kitchen his parents suddenly stopped talking and shuffled about uncomfortably. They were embarrassed. This was ridiculous, thought Eric.

'Mum, what were you talking about?' She didn't reply. 'It was about Leader Boris, wasn't it?' said Eric. 'He is going to die, isn't he? And then what's going to happen? Life won't be the same without Leader Boris. What are we going to do?'

The words poured out faster than Eric had intended, but he was pleased that they had. He was an adult now, and he was entitled to talk about important, grown-up things. He didn't want to be treated like a young bunny anymore. He may have been younger than his parents – although not much younger, it had to be said – but they couldn't go on treating him like a youngster.

Eric's father was clearly shocked by the outburst – so shocked, in fact, that he was lost for words. Eric was pleased by this, but he was a respectful rabbit and had no desire to humiliate his father. He had made his point and although nobody present was ready to admit it publicly, they all realised that from then on, Eric would be treated as an adult, and would need to be closely involved in any discussions about the future of The Warren.

After lunch, Eric made his excuses and left the warren. He had some serious thinking to do, and he preferred to do that alone.

Although Eric would never have described himself as 'a rabbit of the world', he was conscious that, before long, there would be change afoot. Rabbits, he thought, are frightened of change. We all get used to our dependable, comfortable lives in our own warrens, and the prospect of change is daunting.

The more he thought about this, the more that Eric thought this was wrong. Change could be scary, but surely it opened up opportunities too. Just because life had followed one particular course for as long as he could remember, it didn't mean that a different way couldn't be better. His problem was that he didn't know how to go about finding a different path.

Now, as Eric had observed before, rabbits often have big families and although that could cause problems (as at Hoppity's wedding), there were advantages too. Eric had never forgotten the advice that he had received from his teacher at school when he was completing his Graduation Project. Professor Wise, his teacher, had said that if you research and prepare diligently, you will always come up with the right answer.

So, thought Eric, if I am worried about the future, if I am worried about what life will be like once Leader Boris passes away or, worse still, actually dies, then I need to research and prepare for the future, and I will then come up with the right answer. And with a family the size of Eric's, all living in different but nearby warrens, he had the ideal group with whom to begin his research.

With all these ideas swirling about within his mind, Eric began to feel tired and not a little confused. He needed to lie down. And that was good, because all his best ideas seemed to come to him when he was lying down.

A couple of hours later, after Eric had enjoyed a quick nap and then done some very serious thinking, he was ready to begin his research project. He knew that the more ideas that he could get from his various family groups, the more likely he was to be able to formulate a plan for the life of The Warren after Leader Boris was no longer with them.

– Chapter 3 –

The research programme gathers momentum

As far as the research was concerned, there were real benefits for Eric in having a large family – even if he wasn't always entirely clear about how his various family members were related.

Eric codenamed his research programme 'Life after Boris' until he realised that a codename was meant to disguise the real purpose of the project, at which stage he decided to abandon the use of a codename altogether.

In all, there were three separate families living in the various smaller warrens spreading around The Warren where Leader Boris lived with his immediate family. They were called North Warren, South Warren and East Warren. For some reason, there was no West Warren – but nobody could explain why. He would go and see each family in turn, and talk to them to try and understand, hypothetically of course, how they thought matters would evolve should Leader Boris ever decide to 'retire'.

Although Eric was happy in his own mind that this was the right thing to do, he knew that he would have to be very careful in terms of how he went about the research project.

Some of his 'cousins' (they were all called 'cousins' but Eric wasn't entirely sure that they were all his real cousins), were kind and gentle rabbits. Sometimes Eric thought that they were too 'kind and gentle' because they were slow to speak their mind in family debates, but then grumbled about the outcome later. Others were young and rather brash. As his mother sometimes commented, 'They speak first and think afterwards.' She was right of course, but Eric put it down to a lack of breeding – a common problem amongst rabbits.

Amongst his older relatives, there were many who were very set in their ways. They had followed the same routine, day after day, month after month, year after year, and any mention of change was treated with a deep scepticism. Eric sympathised with this to a certain extent. He liked his daily routine; he liked to know where he stood. But he also realised that change was sometimes necessary, and if Leader Boris really was coming to the end of his days, then change was almost inevitable.

So Eric was facing quite a challenge – three very large families within The Warren and, he suspected, quite a diversity of views even within those families. The days of young rabbits being seen and not heard, and automatically respecting the views of their elders, were long gone. This was not going to be a simple task, but nevertheless it was one that Eric was keen to undertake. And so he did.

Eric remembered from his school days how important it was to plan big projects. 'A lack of preparation leads to a lack of focus' was one of Professor Wise's favourite sayings. Eric didn't understand what this phrase meant when he first heard it, but after he got into a terrible muddle in Year 3 at school when he had to research the favourite foods of all his cousins, the point that Professor Wise was driving at soon became clear.

So, the first thing that Eric did was to slip into the sitting room and take a large sheet of paper from his mother's bureau. He felt rather bad about this. He didn't like stealing – except of course when he went shopping in the gardens and allotments, but that was different. His mother had lots of paper for all the lists she made (sometimes Eric thought that she made lists of all her lists) – so he felt sure she wouldn't mind him taking just one sheet.

He went back to his room, shut the door and sat down at his desk. He wrote in large, careful letters: 'Research Project – Life after Boris' at the top of the sheet and then down the left hand margin, he wrote North Warren, South Warren and East Warren. This left most of the page blank for Eric to fill in with the results of his research.

The amount of space that would need to be completed was rather daunting in itself. Eric scratched his head. He wanted to make sure that he asked the same questions to each of the three warrens and he was very aware that he could be quite a forgetful rabbit at times. So he decided that the best thing to do would be to write down the questions so that he could remember them and then go through them one by one in each warren.

But what questions should he ask? What had started as a good idea for a relatively simple research project was turning into quite a challenge. Eric thought about it and realised that, of course, he could just have a bit of a chat with the current leaders of each of the warrens, and then summarise their thoughts later. Nobody would know what the other rabbits had said, and then Eric could use the 'findings' of his research to promote whatever he thought might be the right solution.

The more he thought about this idea, the stronger the temptation became. After all, what was the purpose of the research? Was it to do what was best for The Warren as a whole, or what was best for Eric? As he reflected on this question, Eric said to himself: 'Of course, I must do what is best for The Warren as a whole.' But then, every now and then, a nagging voice in the back of his mind raised some doubts, which troubled young Eric. 'You could be the next leader,' it said. 'Look after number one. It would be good for you *and* good for The Warren.'

Now Eric was not a selfish rabbit, but he certainly was ambitious. Surely, though, he was too young to be the next leader. Poor Eric became quite confused and discombobulated by all these thoughts churning through his mind. In fact, he didn't know what to think at all.

That night, he went to bed, but he couldn't sleep a wink. And then it came to him. There was no need to make a decision now at all. Eric had once heard his father say 'Why make a decision when you can sit on the fence?' He hadn't quite understood what it meant at the time, but now he thought that he did! He would conduct his research – and then decide what to do. With his planning now complete, Eric was ready to begin.

– Chapter 4 –

The North Warren

When he got up in the morning, Eric should have been very tired, but for some reason he wasn't. Either the excitement of starting his new project was making up for the loss of sleep – or perhaps he had slept rather better than he had thought.

Whatever the reason, he was all ready to go and so, after a good breakfast of lettuce, tomato and radish, he got out his large piece of paper (carefully folded up so as to avoid any difficult questions from his mother) and off Eric went to try and talk to Percival in the North Warren.

Percival was a wise, old rabbit. Not quite as wise, or indeed as old, as Leader Boris but nevertheless Percival had been around for as long as Eric could remember, and he therefore felt that a discussion with Percival would be a good place to start.

Eric put his head round the door of the North Warren rather gingerly to see if anyone was in. Eric was a bright and clever young rabbit, but he was not overly confident and he was certainly not the sort of rabbit to go bouncing in to someone else's warren uninvited.

But today his luck was in. Although he couldn't immediately see Percival, Eleanor was there, busily tidying up in the kitchen after breakfast. Eleanor was one of the loveliest rabbits that Eric knew. She had looked after Percival for years and although she was a little prone to gossip, she was always ready to help anyone in need. In fact, her camomile tea and 'Special Eleanor Salads' had a reputation as being the ultimate restoratives for any young rabbit who had either fallen out with one of his friends or, even worse, had a narrow escape from an irate gardener or a bouncy Labrador!

When she saw Eric put his head round the door, Eleanor immediately invited him in and told him to sit down at the kitchen table and make himself at home. 'Now, young Eric,' she said, 'You look as though you have something on your mind. What can I do to help?'

This was just perfect, thought Eric. I can have a nice cup of camomile tea and rather than having a more difficult conversation with Percival, who might wonder why I am asking so many questions, I can chat to Eleanor who will tell me all that I need to know – and probably more besides – without even thinking about why I want all this information.

Eric pulled out a chair and sat down at Eleanor's kitchen table. She put the kettle on and, before he realised what was happening, Eric was pouring his heart out to Eleanor, telling her of all his concerns about what life would be like when Leader Boris was no longer in control and, more importantly, who should succeed him as Leader when there were so many rabbits in the warren, all of whom would have their own ideas and views, and very few of whom would agree with one another.

Before he had finished his second cup of camomile tea, Eric had told Eleanor everything. He had intended to visit each of the warrens and just set the scene of what he thought life could be like after the passing away of Leader Boris. He had planned to hear all the various reactions before mulling them over and making some recommend-ations. But at the very first meeting of his research project, here he was, not only talking to Eleanor rather than Percival, he was also out-lining all the options that he had been considering, and not listening to her views at all.

Eric was soon enjoying the third cup of camomile tea that Eleanor kindly offered him, together with a slice of the quite exquisite carrot cake, for which Eleanor was justly renowned, before taking his leave and heading off.

Eric was very disappointed with himself. Professor Wise would have been even more disappointed, but at least he had moved on now and no longer taught at The Warren. There was one redeeming thought in Eric's mind. The North Warren was the first of the three warrens that Eric had been planning to visit. There were still two more to visit. And he must try harder in future to follow his plans and not get carried away with the moment. Above all, he must not come to any conclusions on the basis of his rather unilateral discussion with the lovely Eleanor.

– Chapter 5 –

The South Warren

Moving on to the South Warren, Eric was firm in his resolve to listen rather than talk. Of course, he would have to explain the background to his research, but that was where he would draw the line.

The South Warren was a very different set up to the North Warren. Whereas Percival enjoyed playing 'The Elder Statesman' in the North Warren, where the other rabbits tended to listen to him, and then do what he said, just because he was popular, old and wise, there was a marked contrast in the warren in which Eric now found himself.

First of all, and as far as Eric could tell, there was no 'Elder Statesman' in this warren. He didn't quite know why. Eric had always assumed that the leader in any warren would be the wise old rabbit who was both popular and respected. It would be a rabbit who had worked hard all his life, initially doing the shopping and then taking on one of the many internal roles, such as teaching the young rabbits, maintaining the warren in tip top condition, or presiding over the disputes that sometimes occurred between rabbit families. These disputes were particularly prevalent when there was some sort of confusion between siblings, half siblings, cousins, aunts, uncles and 'friends'. With such experience such a rabbit would be well prepared to become the 'Elder Statesman', normally in the absence of anyone else.

But in the South Warren it was very different. Eric remembered hearing rumours many years back about an old rabbit (who Eric thought was called Archibald, but he couldn't quite remember) who was 'pushed upstairs'. Eric found this concept very confusing. How could anyone be 'pushed upstairs' when the entire warren was underground?

Eric remembered being very confused about this for a long time, and on the one occasion that he had plucked up courage to ask his father about the fate of poor old Archibald, he was sent to bed without any tea and told not to worry about things that didn't concern him. It was all very confusing for a young rabbit.

As Eric had grown up and become a more worldly rabbit, he gradually understood what had happened in the South Warren – or at least he thought he did. There were two rabbits in the warren, Trevor and Gary, who were well known for being some of the best shoppers around. Whenever they went out together, they always came back with the crunchiest carrots, the biggest beetroots, the most ravishing radishes – and all the girl rabbits just loved Trevor and Gary.

Eric didn't really know Trevor and Gary but he couldn't help feeling a little envy when he heard of their reputation. He knew it was mis-placed envy because they came from a different warren and were that much older than he was, so it wasn't even as though they were turning the heads of the girl rabbits that Eric was trying to woo. But, nevertheless, there was definitely envy in Eric's heart.

Envy is not a good thing. It is not something to be proud of – nor even admit to. Eric's mother used to tell him that, whenever she could see it welling over from Eric's heart. But sometimes he couldn't help himself. It was a bit like jealousy, thought Eric. In fact, it was very like jealousy, but that was probably only because Eric had never quite been able to work out what the difference between envy and jealousy really was.

This envy, though, had turned into respect when Eric heard a few months back that Trevor and Gary had become the joint leaders of the South Warren. Once the rumours that had been circulating for a few days had been confirmed, the other rabbits were talking about the new leaders of the South Warren quite openly and the overall reaction was one of amazement. The South Warren had appointed two (relatively) young rabbits as leaders on the basis of the reputation they had developed carrying out other roles within the warren. They were not old; they were not wise (as far as Eric knew); they were just very good at shopping.

How strange, thought Eric. But as he went into the South Warren through the back door (nowadays, only Trevor and Gary were allowed to use the front door), he was determined to try and understand not only what Trevor and Gary's roles really were, but also what the other rabbits thought about this unusual set up.

Coming through the back door, Eric entered the communal dining room where, despite it being mid-morning and nowhere near a proper meal time, a few of the middle-aged rabbits were sitting around the table with cups of what smelled like mint tea. Two of them were playing cards, one was fast asleep and two others were talking about the new caretaker at the Council allotments.

They all looked up when Eric walked in. All, that is, except the rabbit who was asleep. He snortled a little bit, and shuffled in his chair, but he didn't actually wake up. They were a friendly bunch and invited Eric to join them at the table. He happily did so, but he turned down their offer of a cup of mint tea. Not only was he still awash with Eleanor's three cups of camomile tea, but he also had no intention of washing away the lingering taste of her delicious carrot cake.

Once he was settled at the table, Eric began to explain his mission. He was concerned that Leader Boris might be about to pass away – or worse still to actually die – and he was concerned that no thought had been given as to what was going to happen after Leader Boris was no longer with them. He was therefore talking to some of the rabbit family groups in the other warrens to see whether anyone had any bright ideas for life after Boris.

Well, even before he had finished his explanation of the background, Eric was almost overwhelmed by the flood of ideas. There was so much talking, debating, interrupting and, at times, shouting, that even the sleepy old rabbit soon woke up.

And the one common theme coming through from all these opinions was that they were all different! Some thought that Trevor and Gary were good; some thought they were bad. Most of the rabbits thought that only some of what Trevor and Gary did was good. Some thought that it was impossible for younger rabbits to be leaders; others thought that the task of being a leader was too much for an older rabbit.

The cacophony of sound was almost too much for Eric. The more he heard, the more confused he became. How on earth could he work out the merits – or otherwise – of everything he had heard when there were so many conflicting views. The whole thing was just too confusing for poor Eric. He just didn't know what to do.

At that stage, the effects of the third cup of Eleanor's camomile tea began to make themselves known and so Eric excused himself and left the room. After attending to the call of nature (which in itself was quite a relief), Eric walked around the garden taking deep breaths. This was something that he had learned from his father, who often walked around the garden when all Eric's brothers and sisters were getting a little too noisy and boisterous at bath time. And the deeper the breaths that Eric took, the clearer his thoughts became. And the clearer his thoughts became, the more Eric realised that he needed to go back into the South Warren dining room and ask just a few more questions.

Although Eric knew that Trevor and Gary had become the leaders of the South Warren, and that some of the rabbits had thought that this was a good thing, and some had not, it was not clear to Eric how Trevor and Gary had become the leaders. Had they been elected? Had they been appointed – and, if so, by whom? Or had they just 'become' the leaders, without anyone actually realising why or how? And perhaps most importantly, had there been any consultation with others within the warren who might have had aspirations to becoming the leader themselves?

When Eric went back to the South Warren dining room, peace had returned. The noise had subsided and the rabbits were back doing what they had been doing prior to Eric's interruption. When he came back into the room, they all looked up, wondering what on earth Eric was going to say next, and whether the impact of the next line of questioning was going to be quite as disruptive as the earlier questions had been.

All eyes were on Eric. He coughed politely. He realised that he couldn't ask all the questions that he wanted to ask because, if he did so, the discussion would get totally out of control once again and he would learn nothing. He thought that it would be a much better idea to ask a simple question and then listen intently to the answers. So this is what he did.

It seemed to Eric that the best question to ask would be whether there had been any consultation before Trevor and Gary had been appointed as leaders. Well, talk about opening a floodgate! All of the five rabbits sitting around the table answered simultaneously and, as far as Eric could tell, they all came up with completely different answers.

'We were consulted.' 'We weren't consulted.' 'We were consulted – but nobody listened to our views.' 'They listened to our views – but ignored them.' 'All our views were different – so they couldn't listen to us all.' Once again, Eric began to feel himself becoming totally overwhelmed.

And just as Eric was beginning to wonder what on earth to do next, the front door swung open and who should walk in, with a quite discernible swagger, but Trevor and Gary. The other rabbits immediately fell silent. Eric looked at the table, but could feel himself blush a deeper shade of crimson by the minute. But why was he blushing? He hadn't done anything wrong. Oh dear. Poor old Eric really wasn't very good at this type of situation. What on earth was he going to do?

His dilemma disappeared as Trevor said to him (in what Eric thought was a rather patronising tone): 'Hello there, young Eric. And what can we do for you?' Now Eric was no great academic but the correct use of the English language was important to him. So why had Trevor said 'Hello there'. Why not just 'Hello'? And why did he say 'What can we do for you?' when it was just Trevor talking to him?

The more he thought about it, the more Eric realised that Trevor had the sort of confidence and presence that Eric simply didn't have. Trevor wasn't being difficult or unpleasant. He just had that something about him that enabled him to progress effortlessly to positions that others could only dream about.

Eric suddenly realised that Trevor had asked him a question and he hadn't yet had the courtesy to reply. So, once again, Eric explained the reason behind his research and asked whether Trevor and Gary might have a few minutes to explain their thoughts. 'Of course,' said Trevor. 'Come through to my office, and we can have a nice cup of fruit tea.'

– Chapter 6 –

Tea with Trevor and Gary

When they passed through the green baize door marked 'Private', it was like entering a different world. There was a large mahogany desk covered in important-looking papers and on the other side of the room there was a smaller circular table, with three chairs round it, and a pot of sweetly smelling tea placed exactly in the middle, with three matching cups, one in front of each chair.

'Sit down, sit down,' said Trevor. Eric waited politely, but once Gary had pulled the chair out and sat down, Eric followed suit. 'Now, how can we help?'

Eric was rather confused by this question. He thought that he had already explained the purpose of his research. Perhaps this was a rhetorical question. He had often heard Professor Wise mention rhetorical questions but had never really quite understood what they were. He knew it was something about asking a question, without expecting an answer. Perhaps Trevor didn't expect an answer now.

Just as Eric was turning this over in his mind and contemplating how he should respond, Trevor launched into a long discourse of how he and Gary had become the leaders of the South Warren; why they had been appointed ahead of some of the more experienced rabbits; what the reaction of others in the warren had been and so on and so on.

Eric listened as intently as he could but as Trevor's monologue went on and on, Eric's ability to concentrate reduced by the minute. But even though Eric wasn't able to take in all the detail of what Trevor was saying, an overall impression was gradually forming in his mind. The more he reflected, the clearer the impression became.

The way that Trevor and Gary had assumed control from poor old Archibald was a bit like one of the 'bloodless coups' that Eric used to read about in his history books. History was Eric's favourite subject at school, and he particularly enjoyed modern history, which was just as well, because they didn't seem to have coups in olden times. There had been some discussion before Trevor and Gary had taken over, and some of their friends had clearly supported them, but there didn't appear to have been any elections, or anything democratic like that.

Was this a good way of becoming leader, thought Eric. Trevor must have been reading his mind because within seconds of the thought entering Eric's head, Trevor began on a new tack, addressing the very concern that Eric was considering. 'When we became the leaders,' said Trevor, 'We may not have been voted in, but nobody voted against us, so it was alright.' 'Exactly,' said Gary. 'The point was that everybody was busy, and nobody had time to take on the management role, so we did it ourselves.'

'I see,' said Eric, politely. 'But if everyone was too busy, why weren't you too busy as well?' 'Good question, lad, good question,' said Trevor, once again adopting his rather patronising tone. 'If you need an important job done, ask a busy man – or at least a busy rabbit.'

'But what happened about all the shopping for the warren?' asked Eric. 'If you two were such good shoppers, surely you were missed when you gave up shopping and became the leaders of the warren'. 'We were missed, lad, we were missed,' said Trevor. His repetitive and patronising tone was really beginning to irritate Eric now, but there was nothing that he could say. That would have been rude. 'But management is important, so they just had to train up another young rabbit to do the shopping. He wasn't very good, and it took time to train him, but needs must.'

Needs must what? … thought Eric. He really didn't like Trevor at all. A slight degree of self-satisfaction was fine in an older rabbit, but it was not an attractive trait in someone of Trevor's age. Eric couldn't understand why the other rabbits in the South Warren had allowed poor old Archibald to be 'pushed upstairs' and how they could possibly tolerate Trevor and Gary as joint leaders.

Eric wondered how long they would last as leaders of the South Warren, and indeed what they would do when they too got 'pushed upstairs'. It was one thing for poor old Archibald to be forced out but at least he was of an age that he could enjoy his pipe, slippers and camomile tea, but Eric couldn't see Trevor and Gary lasting very long. And then what would they do? Too young to retire and they would have lost their touch at being the top shoppers. An interesting conundrum, he thought.

The more his thoughts raced ahead, the more Eric realised that he was no longer listening to Trevor's monologue. Trevor realised, too, that he had lost Eric's attention but rather than admitting to this failing on his part, he quickly said that he was a very busy (or did he mean important?) man, and that he would now have to ask Eric to leave as he had many other important things to do as joint leader of the South Warren.

Being dismissed like that did not worry Eric in the slightest. He had learned a great deal during his time in the South Warren and now all he wanted to do was to go home, sit down, think it all through and fill in the empty spaces on his large sheet of paper.

– Chapter 7 –

Another day, another warren

The following morning, with all the information that Eric had gathered from the South Warren now carefully analysed and neatly summarised on the large sheet of paper, and after a good night's sleep, Eric set off to visit the third of the three warrens, the East Warren.

The East Warren was the furthest one from home for Eric, so it took him a few minutes to get there. On his way, he whistled a cheerful tune as he really felt that his research project was beginning to fall into place. A number of good ideas were already formulating in his mind and he thought that he might actually be able to provide some helpful advice to add to the discussion that would inevitably follow when Leader Boris passed away – or, worse still, died.

Eric didn't know a great deal about the East Warren. Being that little bit further from his own warren, he didn't have many friends in the East Warren; in fact, thinking about it, he couldn't think of a single rabbit that he knew there. But that couldn't be right, thought Eric. There must have been a few in his class at Professor Wise's school, but that was really quite a long time ago now, and he certainly couldn't remember any of the names.

As he approached the East Warren, he saw a very beautiful young rabbit. She was so pretty that his heart, having missed a beat, began to beat so loudly that Eric was quite concerned that someone would hear it. He had no idea who this lovely creature was. He was quite sure that he hadn't seen her before, because nobody could ever forget such a gorgeous creature.

He walked past her nonchalantly, trying to look debonair and calm. He rather wished he had put on a smarter shirt this morning – perhaps the new red one with blue polka dots that his mother had made for him last week – but then he hadn't been expecting to see this vision of beauty. And just as he walked past her in the warren, she turned, put her paw on his arm, and said 'Eric … it is Eric, isn't it?'

Eric was almost lost for words, but fortunately he had enough presence about him to respond immediately, even though he had no idea who this young rabbit was. 'It is Eric,' he said. 'How lovely to see you again.' Eric thought that he had handled the situation masterfully. He was now engaged in conversation with this lovely young rabbit, and she had no idea that he hadn't recognised her at all. Or so he thought.

'You didn't recognise me, did you?' said this beautiful apparition. 'I'm Xanthe,' she said. 'We were in the same class at school all those years ago with Professor Wise.' 'Of course we were,' said Eric. 'I remember it well but my, how you have changed. I suppose we have all changed, but you must have changed more than most.'

Before they knew it, they were engaged in a long and interesting discussion, reminiscing about their school days, and what had happened to them since. Their lives had taken them down very different paths and so it was lovely for Eric to hear all the news of old friends with whom he had lost touch.

Their trip down memory lane was becoming so enthralling that Eric quite forgot the real purpose of his visit and when he glanced at his watch, he soon realised that time was running out if he was to achieve the last part of his research that morning. Xanthe had noticed him looking at his watch, and she also noticed the worried furrow that had appeared across his forehead.

'What is the matter?' asked Xanthe in a tender and concerned voice. Beautiful and caring thought Eric. What a perfect combination. He had never experienced true love, but he was beginning to think that he might be about to do so for the very first time.

Eric explained the real purpose of his visit; his concerns about Leader Boris; how he felt that the time was rapidly approaching when Leader Boris might soon pass away – or, worse still, die; and why he was therefore visiting the three warrens to try and understand how they each managed themselves and worked out who their own leaders should be.

Xanthe looked intrigued. A knowing look spread over her beautiful face. 'Haven't you heard about Mr Mole?' she said. 'Mr Mole?' asked Eric. 'What on earth are you talking about?'

'Have you got time for a cup of my very special beetroot and ginger tea?' asked Xanthe. 'I can't help thinking that if we were to sit down for a few minutes so that I could explain what has been happening here in the East Warren, you might even be able to finish off your research without talking to anybody else.'

How wonderful, thought Eric. More time with the lovely Xanthe, and no need to try and get to the leaders of the East Warren, a prospect which he found rather daunting, particularly as he didn't even know who they were. And Xanthe had said something about a mole. How very strange.

– Chapter 8 –

Tea with Xanthe

Eric followed Xanthe into her little kitchen. He sat down at the chair in front of the kitchen table, while she busied herself, putting the kettle on and finding matching cups and saucers. To be honest, beetroot and ginger was not Eric's favourite combination, but he was not going to turn down an invitation from the lovely Xanthe.

Soon, they were sitting together at the kitchen table. Time was marching on and so Eric said to Xanthe, 'Now tell me how the East Warren is run, and particularly about Mr Mole.'

And so Xanthe began … and it was not long before she was in full flow, explaining the chaos caused by the sudden demise of their former leader, Hugo, under the wheels of the smart hatchback that lived in the garage at number 24 Acacia Drive. She went through all the arguments that had ensued, primarily because nobody had anticipated the fate that would befall Hugo (there was no question of him 'passing away', he was definitely dead, not to say two dimensional). And she finished by explaining the ultimate decision to look outside the East Warren for a new leader, which eventually resulted in the appointment of Mr Mole.

Eric was flabbergasted. He had no idea that the East Warren was led by a mole. How extraordinary. Eric knew that moles were very intelligent animals, and he was sure that Mr Mole was a kind, wise and very sensitive mole, but even so. Imagine being told what to do by a mole! It was bad enough being told off by his own mother (particularly now that he was almost adult); and he had huge respect for Leader Boris, because he had always been the leader and so he deserved respect; but to have someone foisted on you as a leader who was not even a rabbit – well, that was unthinkable.

The more he thought about it, the more questions cropped up in Eric's mind. How old was Mr Mole? Where did he live? What did he do before he was appointed as the leader of the East Warren? What did the other senior members of the warren think about it? How did Mr Mole command respect? Indeed, did he command respect at all?

Xanthe and Eric had a long and interesting discussion, covering all these points. Most of it was very helpful for Eric, although at times he became a little confused as to what were facts – and what were little bits of gossipy embellishment that Xanthe had added to make the story more colourful.

As he reflected on everything that he had heard, Eric realised that the decision to appoint an outsider to be the leader of the East Warren was a brave one. It was a decision that had the potential to be very successful – or perhaps a complete disaster. Mr Mole had only been the leader for a few weeks, and so it was perhaps a little early to tell whether or not his appointment was going to work out, but from what Xanthe had been saying, Eric couldn't help thinking that maybe it would have been better if a little more care, a little more thought, and a little bit more discussion had taken place before his appointment. Time would tell, thought Eric.

It had been a lovely morning, thought Eric, as he set off home in time for lunch. Xanthe had given him plenty to think about, and he was going to spend the afternoon filling in his large sheet of paper – and then he would have to start beginning to draw some conclusions.

But it had also been a lovely morning because he had met Xanthe again. She was such a pretty rabbit – and she was intelligent and lovely too. What more could a young rabbit want? And when she put her paw on his arm as he was leaving and said that they must meet up again before too long, Eric felt almost overwhelmed with the emotion of it all.

– Chapter 9 –

Pulling it all together

Eric went home with a spring in his step. Not only had he finished his research, but he had also met the girl he knew he was destined to marry. With his mind racing, Eric reached home before he knew it.

'What's up with you?' asked his mother, as he bounced into the warren. 'What do you mean?' asked Eric, trying to appear sophisticated and nonchalant, but aware that he was already beginning to blush. There was something about being a mother. They were always so perceptive – even when there was very little to perceive. Although on this occasion, perhaps there were some grounds for his mother's enquiring looks.

Eric hadn't told his parents about his research project, or his concerns for Leader Boris, and he didn't feel that the time was right now. So he just mumbled something and nothing, and shuffled off into his room. Once he was sure that his mother was busy in the kitchen and was therefore unlikely to disturb him, he got out the large sheet of paper, and began to fill in all the blanks.

What had been quite a daunting project initially was rapidly becoming a much simpler one. Everything that Eric had learned from his visits to the three warrens was falling into place in his mind and, much more importantly, he was able to translate those thoughts from his mind onto the large sheet of paper.

Xanthe had been truly inspirational. Eric was quite sure that none of this would have been possible had he not bumped into Xanthe. He had always believed in the value of his research project, but now that Xanthe was involved, however casually, it had assumed an added importance. If he produced a really worthwhile document that perhaps the other senior rabbits would take some notice of, his own standing within The Warren would rise inestimably, and he would become an important and noteworthy rabbit – and that might make him 'a good catch'. How fortuitous.

A few minutes later, there was a knock on his bedroom door. 'What are you doing in there, Eric?' called his mother. 'Nothing, really,' he said. 'Just tidying a few things up.' His mother was rather confused. Eric had never tidied anything up in his life. His bedroom was always a complete mess, but his mother always forgave him and did it herself when Eric was out. After all, he was her favourite son – and also he was an excellent shopper.

'Don't you think you ought to go back and see whether Leader Boris needs any more shopping this afternoon?' His mother was right, of course. Mothers normally are, thought Eric. So he completed filling in all the blanks on his large sheet of paper and then headed off to Leader Boris's warren to see whether he was needed.

When he got there, Mrs Cabbage was sitting outside looking very sad – even a little tearful. Mrs Cabbage was a wise old rabbit who had seen a great deal of life – high spots, low spots and most spots in between. Oh dear, thought Eric. This does not bode well.

Eric was a sensitive rabbit and, for all his new found excitement (he only had to think of Xanthe for a shiver to go up his spine), he was very conscious that he needed to be gentle in his approach to Mrs Cabbage.

'Hello, Mrs Cabbage,' said Eric, quietly. 'Is there anything that I can do; any shopping that I can get for Leader Boris or, of course, for you?' 'No thank you, dear,' said Mrs Cabbage in a frail, quiet voice. 'I don't think that there is anything that anyone can do, now. We shall all just have to wait.'

Wait? Wait for what, thought Eric. And then he realised that Mrs Cabbage probably meant that we would have to wait for Leader Boris to pass away – or, worse still, even die. How sad, thought Eric, but his sadness was soon tempered when he thought of Xanthe, the new found love of his life. So he decided to head off back to his warren to begin drawing up the conclusions to his research project.

As he walked home, Eric thought about the next steps. Should he tell his parents – or not? Would they be cross, thinking that he was over-stepping the mark for a young rabbit, or would they be proud of his initiative and respect his commitment to The Warren and his vision for the future? Eric just didn't know, so he decided to go and see Xanthe and see what she thought.

Reaching the East Warren, Eric was hugely relieved to bump into Xanthe almost as soon as he got there. He hadn't wanted to ask anyone where Xanthe was, in case the inevitable blush that would follow his uttering of her name would give away his true – and bliss-ful – feelings for her. After all, she may already have a boyfriend. That would be heartbreaking and was something that Eric didn't want to even think about, but it could be true. Although Eric didn't think that it was. After all, she had put her paw very tenderly on his arm, and no young rabbit would do that if she was already spoken for, surely?

When Xanthe saw Eric, her face broke into a broad smile. This gave Eric's confidence a real boost. She can't have a boyfriend, I'm sure, thought Eric, and in fact he was right. Eric was soon to discover that Xanthe had been courting for some time. However, her intend-ed had been the victim of a nasty motor accident on Acacia Drive, that accident blackspot, a few weeks ago, and she had only recently come out of mourning for him.

Xanthe invited Eric in for a cup of tea – apple and cinnamon this time – and as they sat at her kitchen table, Eric decided to tell her the full story. His concerns for Leader Boris; the danger of a power vacuum; how the leaders of the different warrens had taken on their roles by a variety of diverse routes; and how he felt that some order and process should be put in place so as to ensure that the best solution could be achieved in Life after Boris.

Xanthe listened intently. She could feel herself swelling with pride that her new boyfriend (or was she being just a little presumptious to think of Eric as her boyfriend?) had thought through such complex and challenging issues and was quite clearly set on a course that would lead to him becoming a very important rabbit within the overall warren structure.

The more she listened, the more convinced Xanthe became that Eric was on to something here. It didn't matter how old you were, or where your background lay. If someone has an idea that could benefit the warren as a whole, that idea should be put forward, and the powers that be should listen to it carefully and studiously. But how best to achieve this?

First things first, thought Xanthe. Eric would need to write a report summarising his research findings, but it needed to be short and concise, otherwise nobody would read it. Also, Eric needed to get his parents' support, as they would need to know what Eric was up to before he disappeared into his room to work on his report.

It soon became clear that a five stage process lay ahead for Eric. First, he needed to get home as soon as possible. The sooner he started, the sooner he would finish. Secondly, he would need to take his parents into his confidence and tell them what he had been doing – and what his plans were. Thirdly, he had to write the report. Then he would need to pass it to all the important rabbits in The Warren – and possibly some of the less important ones too – and finally he would need to ensure that some decisive action resulted from his recommendations. Quite a challenge indeed!

The first stage was easy; the next was a little harder; and they then became progressively more difficult. But when Xanthe said that she would be incredibly proud of Eric if he could successfully achieve all five stages, Eric set off with such determination that he knew he would succeed.

– Chapter 10 –

The five stage process

Eric had the five stages indelibly printed on his mind. Professor Wise frequently referred to 'Five Stage Processes' in his school lessons (although sometimes they only had three or four stages and Eric never quite understood why they were still called 'Five Stage Processes', but never mind).

The only one that Eric remembered was the 'Five Stage Shopping Process' because this was the one that every young rabbit had to know by heart before leaving school. The other ones were more complicated – and arguably less important – and so very few of the young rabbits actually remembered them.

Eric thought that to remember the shopping one would be a good start, and perhaps he could even model his own research findings on such a process. Now, thought Eric, what were the five stages?

1) Get a shopping list
2) Go to the allotment
3) Choose the vegetables
4) Check that the coast is clear
5) Hurry home

He knew those were the right stages, but Eric couldn't remember which order they came in. Should the fourth stage be the second? It could make sense in either place, so he supposed that it didn't matter too much.

Anyway, all that thinking was something of a diversion. Eric needed to get through his own five stage process, and the first two stages were getting home and then telling his parents of his plans.

Eric was soon home and luckily his parents were both sitting at the kitchen table, having a nice cup of apple and camomile tea, with a small slice of carrot cake. This was good news because Eric knew that when the carrot cake came out, his mother was happy, and his father would be put in a good mood by the bonus of cake for tea.

So Eric grasped the nettle and came straight out, telling his parents all about his concerns for Leader Boris, his research project, and how he was about to pull it all together and then write his report. He left out the details of 'borrowing' a large sheet of his mother's paper, and also his feelings for Xanthe. Eric's experience of older rabbits in general and his parents in particular was such that he knew that they could only take on board a few shocks at a time!

The words tumbled out of Eric's mouth like a torrent. The more he talked, the more he elaborated – although he was always careful to gloss over the parts that he had decided were best left unsaid. And, much to his surprise and relief, his parents appeared to take it all on board and be very understanding, supportive and even impressed with his approach.

What a relief, thought Eric. It just shows that even the most difficult situation can be overcome with careful planning, openness and honesty. And then he thought about his only partial disclosure, and felt just a little guilty. But he soon realised that he had not been actually dishonest, so that was alright, he decided.

Encouraged by his parents' support, or at least the absence of any suggestion that he should not pursue his project, which was tantamount to support, Eric headed off to his room to begin the third stage of the Five Stage Process – writing the report.

– Chapter 11 –

Writing the report

Eric was very conscious of Xanthe's advice. Keep the report short – otherwise nobody will read it. Eric liked this idea, not only because it came from Xanthe and he would have done anything, but anything, that Xanthe had suggested, but also because Eric didn't like the idea of writing a long report. Words were not Eric's forte and, as far as he was concerned, the shorter the better.

Taking out the large sheet of paper that he had 'borrowed' from his mother, Eric looked at all his notes and after a little bit of head scratching and careful rumination, his ideas gradually began to fall into place. Looking at the three warrens under the control of Leader Boris, it was quite clear that there were three very different scenarios.

In the North Warren, Percival was a solid, respected leader. But it was clear that he was only in the position of leader because he was old and had been a 'good chap' in his younger years. Did that make him a good leader? Perhaps, thought Eric, but not necessarily. And in his discussions with others in the North Warren, it was clear that there were mixed views. Everyone seemed to like Percival, but not everyone thought that he was a good leader.

Perhaps more telling were the comments that Eric had picked up, particularly amongst some of the middle-aged rabbits in the North Warren, that there had not really been any discussion before Percival had just 'assumed' the role of leader. They felt that more should have been done to consult within the warren before a decision had been made. And Eric, who was quite perceptive despite his apparent youth and lack of experience, also felt that if that consultation had taken place, more of the apparently disgruntled middle-aged rabbits might have been more supportive of Percival in his leadership role.

Looking at the South Warren, it was clear that Gary and Trevor were very different from Percival. But in terms of leadership, were they better or worse, thought Eric? He pondered this for a while, and the more he thought about it, the more confused he became. Eric didn't like being confused. If he was to deliver the definitive report about the future leadership of The Warren, he needed to be offering clear and decisive solutions, not confused thinking.

This worried Eric so he decided to have a quiet lie down to try and get his thoughts in order. He found his mind drifting off to think about Xanthe – what a pleasant diversion – but he kept trying to refocus his mind to the problem in hand.

And then it came to him. The situation was exactly the same as in the North Warren with Percival, albeit in a different context. It was clear that Gary and Trevor were good leaders, who had the best interests of The Warren at heart. They were a bit young and pushy – and very sharply dressed – which was not everyone's cup of tea, but they were, for the most part at least, respected as leaders.

Any rumblings of discontent in the South Warren did seem to come from the middle-aged rabbits who, just like in the North Warren, seemed to feel that Gary and Trevor had assumed the role of leaders without there having been sufficient or appropriate consultation. Interesting, thought Eric.

Now, what about Mr Mole in the East Warren? Again, Eric stroked his chin. It was certainly quite a different approach to appoint a mole to be a leader in a rabbit's warren. The very idea would have been unthinkable not so long ago – and was probably still unthinkable to many of the middle-aged rabbits today. Middle-aged rabbits, thought Eric. Why do middle-aged rabbits keep coming into my mind?

Eric tried to recall his conversations with Xanthe. He wished he hadn't been so distracted by her beauty and charm – but unfortunately he had been. Such is life for a young, lovesick rabbit. And then, once again, his thoughts began to fall into place.

Nothing that Xanthe had said, nor anything that the other rabbits in the East Warren had either said or implied, was essentially critical of Mr Mole. He was recognised as being a solid, dependable leader who had brought with him huge amounts of experience from his former life as King Mole. (One rabbit had commented that Mr Mole had not liked the transition from being King Mole to mere Mr Mole but Eric put this down to sour grapes because the rabbit who had made that comment was one of those who may have had aspirations to becoming the new leader before Mr Mole had been appointed.)

However, once again it became clear that Mr Mole had been appointed without there having been very much consultation. The powers that be within the East Warren had taken the bold and, in Eric's view, commendably far-sighted decision to appoint a very different leader, but they hadn't involved many others in the decision, and were now paying the price for not having gained the support of the masses. Interesting, thought Eric again.

With the report now written, Eric thought that he had done enough for one day and lay down on his bed, closed his eyes, and thought about Xanthe. A hard day's work and now, sweet dreams. What a good day.

– Chapter 12 –

Sharing the report

The next morning, Eric woke early. In fact, he was not entirely sure that he had slept very well at all. He was happily excited on two fronts, experiencing relief at having written his report and joy at having met the lovely Xanthe. The combination had not resulted in a peaceful night's sleep.

Nevertheless, a good breakfast of fruit, honey and some camomile tea (and possibly a little adrenalin) had set him up well and soon he was off to distribute the copies of his report. As he was about to leave home, his mother stopped him and said: 'You do know how proud your father and I are of you, don't you Eric. What you are doing is really worthwhile for us all. But don't rush things. Nothing must happen until Leader Boris has passed away.'

Eric thought about what his mother had said and, of course, she was right. Mothers normally are, he thought. The last thing that he wanted to do was to be insensitive at a difficult time for The Warren in general and for Leader Boris's family in particular. But he also felt that plans should be put in place before they were needed, rather than after the crisis had emerged. Tricky, thought Eric, before he had a brilliant idea. What a perfect excuse to go and see Xanthe. He could ask her what she thought. And he respected her opinions too.

So off Eric trotted to the East Warren, eagerly looking forward to seeing Xanthe again. With such a spring in his step, he was unaware initially of the other rabbits who were going to and fro in a very glum and sombre mood. They were all looking at the ground and there were none of the usual cheery hellos with which friends would normally greet one another as they went about their daily business. How strange, thought Eric.

When he reached the East Warren, he went to find Xanthe straight away and found her dabbing her eyes with a large red and white spotted handkerchief. 'My darling,' said Eric, putting his arm around her, 'What on earth is the matter?' 'Haven't you heard?' said Xanthe. 'Leader Boris passed away in the night.'

Eric's mind raced ahead. This was, of course, tragic news, but it had also given him the opportunity to put his arm round Xanthe and call her 'darling', neither of which she had objected to. Every cloud has a silver lining, thought Eric. But those were shallow thoughts, he realised. The Warren was facing a crisis; it was without a leader, and each of the smaller warrens would be wanting to put their own man forward.

There was no time to lose. Eric needed to get his report out – and he needed to get it out now, albeit with care and sensitivity. And that is exactly what he did. As soon as he had conveyed his condolences to Leader Boris's widow, and also to Mrs Cabbage, he took copies of his report to Percival, Gary and Trevor and also to Mr Mole. It has to be said that despite their initial surprise at being offered such a document so soon after the passing away – nobody yet knew whether Leader Boris had actually died – of their leader, they were certainly impressed and all agreed to meet at 5.00 pm that day in Xanthe's parlour in the East Warren.

Eric could hardly believe his luck. Timing is everything, he thought, and with a certain amount of judgement and more than a little luck, not only did he have the leaders of each of the three warrens coming to a meeting that he would facilitate, but it would also be held in the parlour of the most beautiful rabbit in The Warren, with whom he was now head over heels in love. Brilliant.

– Chapter 13 –

The leadership summit

Well ahead of the appointed meeting time, Eric was with Xanthe in the East Warren, preparing the table and chairs and making sure everything was ready in the parlour. Xanthe was busy in the kitchen, preparing a selection of teas and one of her famous carrot cakes. Her feelings for Eric were now as strong as his were for her, and she was not going to let him down.

Despite all the urgency caused by the demise of Leader Boris and the excitement of what he now believed really was true love, Eric remained focused. The leadership summit was clearly a very important meeting that he was now in a position to facilitate, but what was he hoping to achieve from it? He was simply a young rabbit who happened to be working on the right project at the right time. Or was he? Was there a bigger opportunity here? Perhaps there was.

Eric went into the kitchen and said to Xanthe that he would like to lie down and gather his thoughts. Xanthe blushed demurely, but said that would be fine and led him to her bedroom. She quickly straightened the bed cover but then slipped away, leaving Eric to himself. Eric really wanted to concentrate, but found it almost impossible to do so with the sweet fragrance of Xanthe's perfume lingering in the air – and her little camisole draped enchantingly over the back of her chair.

Soon, though, he pulled himself together and he began to assemble his thoughts. Professor Wise's words came back to him. 'You need a Five Stage Process'. What better opportunity than now to instigate a new five stage process, or perhaps even create a business model. Eric didn't quite know what a business model was, but this seemed like the ideal time to create one.

The more he thought about it, the clearer things became. The Warren is made up of three smaller warrens, North, South and East. (Whatever *did* happen to the West Warren?) Each has a leader – or leaders in the case of Gary and Trevor. Each leader is quite good, but they don't have widespread support within their own warren because the consultation process prior to their appointment was flawed – assuming that it happened at all. Therefore, each of the current leaders have strong arguments to support their nomination, but do they have a sufficiently strong mandate to succeed Leader Boris?

Should The Warren go with one of the existing leaders, or would it be better to plump for someone new? But, if it was someone new, who on earth could that be? There were no logical candidates, thought Eric. Some were too old; some were too busy; some did not command the respect that they thought they did; and some were simply unsuitable.

Eric would need to think outside the box. And, all of a sudden, something struck him like a flash of lightning. (Not many rabbits know what a flash of lightning is, because they live underground and lightning doesn't go underground. Eric, however, had been caught in a huge storm during one of his shopping trips and had seen a tree being split into two when it had been struck – so he knew exactly what lightning was.)

Possibly, just possibly, Eric himself could be a candidate.

Everything was well prepared before the leaders arrived. Percival was the first to put his head through the door. 'Hello, my dear,' he said to Xanthe. 'So kind of you to allow us to meet here. Very discreet at this difficult time, and with the prospect of your famous carrot cake … well, how could I refuse?' Xanthe was very touched. She had a very soft spot for Percival, even though he did have a reputation for being something of a bumbling old fool.

Mr Mole was the next to arrive. Being relatively new to The Warren, he was more formal and, of course, very polite and correct. He moved into the parlour and was sitting, chatting to Percival when Gary and

Trevor arrived with a large amount of brash self-importance, and rather less dignity and courtesy. No surprises there, thought Eric.

Once Xanthe had served her carrot cake and a selection of teas, she quietly withdrew and left the leaders (and Eric) to get on with their meeting – although Eric did rather suspect that she was listening at the door. This didn't worry him at all as he rather hoped that she might be quite proud of him if she could hear how he was conducting the meeting.

The meeting itself went exactly as Eric had hoped. Tributes were paid to Leader Boris; the issue of leadership succession was discussed; and it very soon became perfectly clear to Eric that all those present were angling for the top job, without wishing to appear too pushy by putting themselves forward. Perhaps inevitably, Gary and Trevor were the most pushy, but as neither wanted to give way to the other, their progress was limited.

Eric sat and listened. He knew that any good chairman or facilitator should listen and manage the meeting, but not get too dragged into the conversation. The temptation to become involved was strong, but he fought it vigorously, knowing his time would come … and eventually it did.

Just after Xanthe had been in with a fresh pot of tea, and some more slices of her renowned carrot cake (much to Percival's delight), it seemed as though an impasse had been reached. Nobody dared to make the first move to put themselves forward as Leader Boris's successor, and so the conversation ground to a halt with an awkward silence. This was Eric's moment – and he grasped it. Timing is everything, he reminded himself. So he let the silence continue just long enough for the others to begin to feel really uncomfortable, and then he played his trump card, something that he had been rehearsing carefully in his mind.

'I can see that this is all very difficult for you,' said Eric. 'You all have important roles, and if you were to give them up to succeed Leader Boris, that would leave quite a void within your own warrens. Furthermore, anyone who is appointed to lead The Warren must have as widespread support as possible to ensure that he or she (the 'or she' was added for the benefit of Xanthe, just in case she was still listening at the door) is able to guide The Warren through the next stage of its development.

'We must also not forget that there may be something of an issue with some of the residents if the next leader is too closely aligned with the current leadership of just one of the warrens.'

The four leaders all mumbled their agreement. They didn't like the way this conversation was going, but they couldn't see any way of objecting, without putting themselves in an unfavourable light. Eric recognised their discomfort and realised that he was gaining the upper hand. He knew he had to keep going. He could hardly believe how bold he was being in front of four people who just a few days ago he didn't really know. Indeed, if he had known them, he would have treated them with a level of respect that would have probably meant that he wouldn't have even dared to speak to them.

Keeping the initiative, Eric said: 'I would like to make a suggestion. I would not be considered as a leadership contender by the other rabbits in The Warren. And it has become perfectly clear to me that all the members of our families in The Warren do like to be consulted before any major decisions are taken. In fact, so long as they are properly and thoughtfully consulted, they often don't mind about the actual decision that is taken! Therefore, why don't you all allow me to conduct some research amongst all the warrens and report back to you with my findings at this time tomorrow?'

How could anyone argue against such an approach, thought Eric? In fact, it was a masterstroke. Eric had gained total control of the process. All he needed to do now was to go through a consultation process with the rabbits within the three warrens and before the current leaders could do anything about it, his choice would be the new leader in succession to Leader Boris. And if he couldn't think of anyone other than himself to assume the role of leader, so be it.

And then he would ask Xanthe to marry him. What girl would turn down a proposal of marriage from the Leader of The Warren? Everything was falling into place. Eric had to pinch himself to make sure that he was not dreaming.

– Chapter 14 –

Action research

Eric had heard Professor Wise talk about the concept of Action Research. At the time, he hadn't fully understood what it meant, but now it was beginning to become a little clearer. 'Essentially,' he explained to Xanthe as he sat at her kitchen table after the other leaders had left, 'A researcher can determine a particular course of action by conducting research among a defined group of stakeholders in such a way that the research audience begin to buy in and support the views of the researcher.'

Xanthe nodded wisely, despite having absolutely no idea what Eric was talking about. She was completely lost, but she didn't want to appear dim in front of a rabbit who she was rapidly thinking might very soon become her husband. He was young, good looking, a renowned shopper and now, it seemed, quite an astute politician too.

Just imagine if he really did become the Leader of the Warren and she then became his wife. What a party there would be. A big dinner followed by singing and dancing. Xanthe would have a new dress, especially for the occasion, and Eric would look so handsome in a new, brightly coloured waistcoat. How marvellous. Her mother would be so proud of her. It was just such a shame she didn't know who her father was, but that's rabbits for you.

Eric thought more and more about Action Research and decided that this was an important way of achieving consensus about the choice of a new leader. And so, early the next morning Eric began a series of three meetings, one in each of the warrens. Each meeting followed a very similar pattern. First of all, everyone shared their grief for the late Leader Boris. Although the distinction between passing away and dying remained a mystery to Eric, it did seem fairly clear now that Leader Boris would not be seen again and so it had to be assumed that he had died.

Once platitudes had been exchanged, Eric explained to the assembled groups that he was acting on behalf of Percival, Gary and Trevor and Mr Mole to understand who the rabbits would like to see succeed Leader Boris – and at each meeting the groups grew in size as word spread around the warrens about exactly what it was that Eric was researching.

Eric gave plenty of time to all those present to express their views but, as the researcher and group facilitator, he also felt that it was incumbent on him to ensure that the debate remained focused and in line with his brief … and this of course gave Eric the opportunity to emphasise a few key points.

These points were not particularly complex but, perhaps unsurprisingly as Eric was growing in confidence and ambition as the day wore on, they were very similar. To each of the groups, Eric emphasised the high regard in which he held their respective leaders. The rabbits liked this – because there was always intense rivalry between the warrens, and particularly between the South and the North Warren.

But it did also help to serve the point that Eric was seeking to make that to take away a leader who was performing so well in his own warren would perhaps be a mistake.

He also made the point that, in selecting a new Leader, it was important to consult as widely as possible. Again, there was much applause for such an enlightened approach … and a number of the middle-aged rabbits also registered that they had not been consulted in the past, making the approach being suggested by Eric sound all the more attractive.

And finally, in his efforts to be fair to each of the individual warrens, Eric questioned whether it was fair to select one of the existing leaders, or whether The Warren should be looking afresh. Again, it became clear to Eric that no rabbit would vote for a leader that came from another warren, and those middle-aged rabbits who felt that they had been ignored in the past would not even vote for a leader from their own warren. Never before had there been so much call for change.

Some of the more astute rabbits in each of the warrens asked who might succeed Boris, particularly if none of the existing leaders were going to get enough support from The Warren as a whole. 'That's a difficult question,' said Eric, scratching his head and trying to look genuinely perplexed. 'It is beginning to look as though we are going to have to look outside the box. The consensus does appear to be that we should find someone from within our Warren, who does not have too onerous a role at the moment and who has not been tarnished with too much history of leadership. Who on earth could that be?'

And at each of the three meetings in the different warrens, at various stages of the discussion, somebody said 'What about you, Eric?' It couldn't have been scripted better. Admittedly, in the East Warren, it was the lovely Xanthe who had raised the possibility of Eric becoming Leader, but that was fine, because nobody knew of their blossoming relationship and so no suspicions were aroused.

In just a matter of days, Eric was being propelled from being just another young rabbit, to a potential Leader for the entire Warren. He couldn't really get his head round this, but he knew that it was certainly very exciting!

– Chapter 15 –

Decisions are taken

That evening at 5.00 pm, exactly 24 hours after the previous meeting, the four leaders came to Xanthe's parlour to hear the results of Eric's research. But this time, the mood of the meeting was very different. Each of the leaders had made their own informal soundings within the warrens and not even the lure of Xanthe's cake could raise the gloom that the four of them felt. Because, of course, although none of them had gone public about their aspirations to be the next Leader, they had all secretly harboured a desire to succeed Leader Boris.

But the writing was very clearly on the wall. They had all fallen into the trap that Eric had, perhaps inadvertently, set them. By asking him to carry out some research, they had only succeeded in swinging the electorate away from the established candidates … towards the researcher himself. Action Research in action!

Pride is a terrible thing, particularly among rabbits, and in their attempts to avoid the humiliation of defeat and to make light of the situation, Percival, Gary, Trevor and Mr Mole all in turn said that they had decided not to stand as a possible successor to Leader Boris. Percival said that he was too old; Gary and Trevor said that they still had a big task ahead of them in their warren; and Mr Mole said that he could not contemplate a change so soon after having taken up the leadership of the East Warren.

'Oh dear,' said Eric, with deceptively apparent sincerity. 'Where does that leave us?' There was an uncomfortable silence. Mr Mole coughed awkwardly; Trevor scowled; Gary looked so angry that he was about to explode; and good old Percival, who was never a serious contender for the top spot anyway, said in his gentle tones: 'Eric, I have heard some very positive things about you over the last 24 hours. You have shown yourself to be a true and sensitive leader, demonstrating many of the qualities that we need to make our great Warren an even better place in the years ahead. We think that you should take over as our Leader.'

Eric had heard his mother say that she had almost burst with pride on the day that Eric had graduated from school. Fortunately, she didn't – the mess would have been ghastly – but Eric was now seriously concerned that he might do so himself. He was so proud. To be elected Leader at his relatively young age was unprecedented.

He mustn't get ahead of himself, he thought. He didn't want to appear too keen, nor did he want to reveal to the other leaders that he had already anticipated the offer that Percival had just made to him. So he appeared suitably shocked and very flattered – before accepting almost immediately. Almost at once, he realised that he had been a little too quick in his acceptance, but he thought that he had got away with it as the others did not seem to react.

His mind really began to race now. He would have to move from his family home in the North Warren to the Leader's residence, and of course he would need a wife both to provide wise counsel when he was confronted with tricky dilemmas, and also to accompany him to dinners and other formal occasions.

Eric couldn't wait for the leaders to leave, but fortunately they did so, fairly soon afterwards. After all, there was little left to discuss. And as Eric opened the door of the parlour, Xanthe quickly scuttled away as she had quite clearly been listening to every word of the discussion.

As soon as the door had closed behind the leaders, she threw her paws around Eric's neck and gave him the biggest, snuggliest hug that Eric had ever had. Now it was time for there to be tears in his eyes as he went down on to one knee and asked Xanthe to marry him and become the new Leader's consort.

'I will,' said Xanthe and, because they had gone through some careful processes, not to ensure that the right Leader had been chosen, but to ensure that all the rabbits had felt involved in the selection and decision-making process, they lived happily ever after.

THE END